T0080988

Piano

Duets for Fun

Duo-Schatzkiste

Original Works from the Classical to the Modern Era
Originalwerke von der Klassik bis zur Moderne

for Piano Duet
für Klavier vierhändig

Edited by / Herausgegeben von
Monika Twelsiek

ED 23341
ISMN 979-0-001-21284-7
ISBN 978-3-7957-2180-0

Cover design by www.adamhaystudio.com
Cover photography: iStockphoto.com

www.schott-music.com

Mainz · London · Madrid · Paris · New York · Tokyo · Beijing
© 2022 Schott Music GmbH & Co. KG, Mainz · Printed in Germany

Vorwort

Sich die Tastatur eines Klaviers zu teilen und gemeinsam – mit vier Händen – darauf zu spielen, ist ein lohnendes Abenteuer. Berühmte Paare hat es gegeben, von denen man weiß, dass sie mit Vergnügen im Duo Klavier gespielt haben: Wolfgang Amadeus Mozart und seine Schwester Nannerl gingen schon als Kinder gemeinsam auf Konzertreise. Felix Mendelssohn komponierte für sich und seine Schwester Fanny, Johannes Brahms musizierte gemeinsam mit Clara Schumann auf einem Klavier.

Die Anfänge der vierhändigen Klaviermusik liegen im Dunkeln. Erste Handschriften stammen aus dem 17. Jahrhundert. Die Tastatur hatte aber in früher Zeit einen so geringen Umfang, dass das gemeinsame Spiel – außer für Liebespaare – sehr unbequem war. Daher schrieb man zunächst wie für zwei Solisten, die sich im Dialog am Instrument ablösten (in den Stücken von Daniel Gottlob Türk kann man diese Praxis noch gut beobachten). Erst gegen Ende des 18. Jahrhunderts gelang es dem erst neunjährigen Mozart im Finale seiner Sonate KV 19 erstmalig, die klanglichen Möglichkeiten des Klaviers im vierhändigen Spiel voll zur Geltung zu bringen.

Von der Zeit der Wiener Klassik, der Romantik bis zur heutigen Zeit erfreut sich das vierhändige Spiel großer Beliebtheit. Anton Diabelli, Cornelius Gurlitt und Joseph Haydn komponierten für Lehrer und Schüler, Franz Schubert musizierte seine Ländler gemeinsam mit Freunden, Robert Schumann schrieb vierhändige Stücke für seine Frau und seine Tochter Julie. Bei der gemeinsamen Eroberung der Tastatur gibt es nun keine Tabus mehr: die Hände der Spieler greifen übereinander, beiden gehört das gesamte „Spielfeld", jeder Part kann führende Melodie oder zurückhaltende Begleitung sein, beide Spieler können abwechselnd das Pedal übernehmen. Die gesamte Klangfülle des Klaviers wird genutzt.

Unsere „Schatzkiste" enthält – in chronologischer Ordnung – leichte vierhändige originale Klavierwerke, einige in der Bearbeitung bedeutender Zeitgenossen (Mozart in der Bearbeitung von Christian Gottlob Neefe, dem Lehrer Beethovens, Schumann in der Bearbeitung von Theodor Kirchner, selbst ein bedeutender Komponist, Schubert in der Bearbeitung von Johannes Brahms). Die frühsten Werke stammen aus dem 18. Jahrhundert, die jüngsten aus unserer Zeit. Stilistisch reichen die Werke von der Klassik über die Romantik bis zur Stilrichtung des Jazz-Rock-Pop. Auch ein improvisatorisches, teilweise grafisch notiertes Stück (Christoph Hempels „Unheimliche Höhlenmusik") bereichert die Sammlung. Allen Werken gemeinsam ist die leichte Spielbarkeit. Auch die manchmal etwas anspruchsvolleren Secondo-Parts sind für Klavierschüler und Laien gut erreichbar.

Viel Freude beim Öffnen der „Schatzkiste" und beim gemeinsamen Spiel auf einem Klavier wünscht

Monika Twelsiek

Preface

Sitting together at a piano keyboard to play duets is a rewarding adventure. There have indeed been some famous duos known to have enjoyed playing piano duets: Wolfgang Amadeus Mozart and his sister Nannerl went on concert tours together as children; Felix Mendelssohn wrote music for himself and his sister Fanny; Johannes Brahms played the piano sitting beside Clara Schumann.

The origins of piano duets are obscure. The earliest manuscripts date from the 17th Century. Early keyboards had such a limited range, however, that playing alongside one another would have been very uncomfortable – except for lovers! Early compositions were therefore designed for two soloists taking turns at the instrument (this practice may be observed in pieces by Daniel Gottlob Türk). Not until the second half of the 18th Century would Mozart, then aged only nine, show off the rich potential of the piano duet in the Finale of his Sonata KV 19.

From the days of Viennese Classicism and the Romantic era until the present day, piano duets have remained very popular. Anton Diabelli, Cornelius Gurlitt and Joseph Haydn wrote pieces for teachers to play with pupils; Franz Schubert would play his Ländler with friends; Robert Schumann wrote piano duets for his wife and daughter Julie. In mastering the keyboard together there are no taboos left: players may reach across one another's hands as the terrain belongs to both equally; either part may lead with the melody or adopt an accompanying role; players can take it in turns to use the pedal. The full range of sounds on the piano can be explored.

Our 'treasure chest' contains – in chronological order – easy original piano pieces, some of them arranged as duets by well-known contemporaries (Mozart in an arrangement by Christian Gottlob Neefe, Beethoven's teacher, Schumann arranged by Theodor Kirchner, a successful composer himself, Schubert arranged by Johannes Brahms). The earliest pieces are from the 18th Century and the most recent are from the modern era. Stylistically these pieces range from Classical to Romantic, through to jazz, rock and pop. The collection even features an improvisatory piece with partly graphic notation (Christoph Hempel's 'Eerie Cave Music'). What all the pieces have in common is their approachability. Even the sometimes more demanding Secondo parts are well within the range of piano students and amateur players.

Have fun playing the piano together!

Monika Twelsiek
Translation Julia Rushworth

Inhalt / Contents

Secondo

Duettino II

Johann Baptist Vanhal
1739–1813

© 2014 Schott Music GmbH & Co. KG, Mainz
aus / from: J. B. Vanhal: 24 kleine Duette / 24 Little Duets, Schott ED 9027

Duettino II

Johann Baptist Vanhal
1739–1813

Duettino III

Johann Baptist Vanhal

aus / from: J. B. Vanhal: 24 kleine Duette / 24 Little Duets, Schott ED 9027

Duettino III

Johann Baptist Vanhal

aus / from: J. B. Vanhal: 24 kleine Duette / 24 Little Duets, Schott ED 9027

Sieh, nun dreht es sich im Zirkel

Look, It's Turning in Circles Now

Daniel Gottlob Türk
1750–1813

D. C. al Fine

Sieh, nun dreht es sich im Zirkel

Look, It's Turning in Circles Now

Daniel Gottlob Türk
1750–1813

Allegro

Fine

D. C. al Fine

Spute dich, liebe Susanna!

Hurry, Dear Susanna!

Daniel Gottlob Türk

Tempo di Gavotta

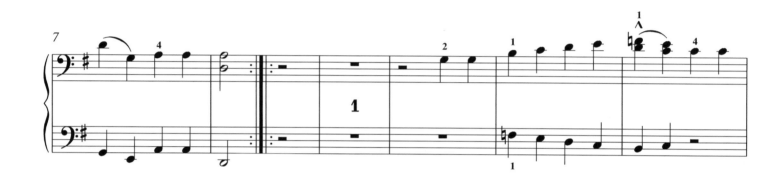

Spute dich, liebe Susanna!

Hurry, Dear Susanna!

Daniel Gottlob Türk

Tempo di Gavotta

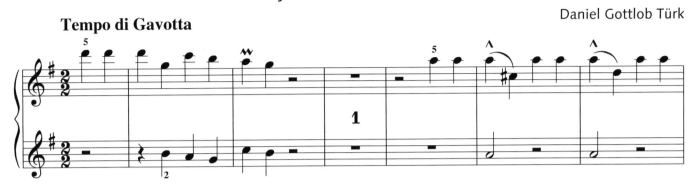

Ich bin so glücklich, bin so froh

I am so Happy, I am so Glad

Daniel Gottlob Türk

D. C. al Fine

Ich bin so glücklich, bin so froh

I am so Happy, I am so Glad

Daniel Gottlob Türk

D. C. al Fine

Moll und Dur
Minor and Major

Daniel Gottlob Türk

Allegro, ma innocentamente (♩. = 66)

Fine

Medesimo tempo *)

Allegro da capo al Fine

*) Medesimo tempo (ital. „dasselbe Tempo") bedeutet: im gleichen Tempo weiter spielen
  Medesimo tempo (ital. "same tempo") means: the following movement should be played at the same tempo as the last

Moll und Dur
Minor and Major

Daniel Gottlob Türk

Allegro, ma innocentamente (♩. = 66)

Fine

Medesimo tempo *)

Allegro da capo al Fine

*) Medesimo tempo (ital. „dasselbe Tempo") bedeutet: im gleichen Tempo weiter spielen
   Medesimo tempo (ital. "same tempo") means: the following movement should be played at the same tempo as the last

Das klinget so herrlich
That sounds so Glorious

aus der Oper „Die Zauberflöte" / "The Magic Flute"

Wolfgang Amadeus Mozart
1756–1791
Arr.: Christian Gottlob Neefe

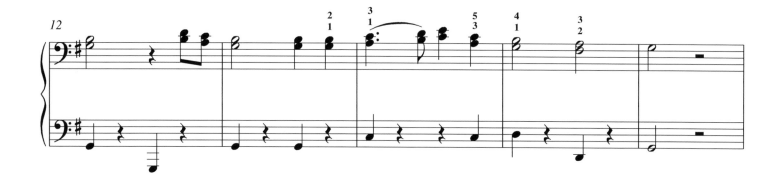

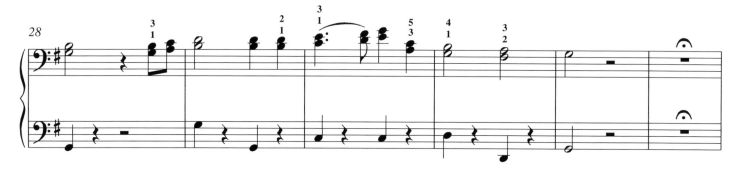

aus / from: Joh. Chr. Neefe, 6 leichte Stücke aus der Oper „Die Zauberflöte" / 6 Easy Pieces from the Opera "The Magic Flute", Schott ED 9949

Das klinget so herrlich
That sounds so Glorious

aus der Oper „Die Zauberflöte" / "The Magic Flute"

Wolfgang Amadeus Mozart
1756–1791
Arr.: Christian Gottlob Neefe

aus / from: Joh. Chr. Neefe, 6 leichte Stücke aus der Oper „Die Zauberflöte" / 6 Easy Pieces from the Opera "The Magic Flute", Schott ED 9949

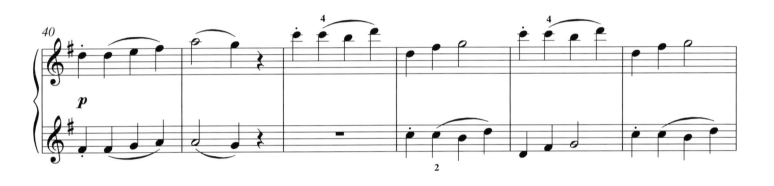

Allegretto

Anton Diabelli
1781–1858

aus / from: A. Diabelli: Melodische Übungsstücke / Melodic Exercises, op. 149, Schott ED 9009

Allegretto

Anton Diabelli
1781–1858

aus / from: A. Diabelli: Melodische Übungsstücke / Melodic Exercises, op. 149, Schott ED 9009

Romanza
g-Moll / G minor

Anton Diabelli

aus / from: A. Diabelli: Melodische Übungsstücke / Melodic Exercises, op. 149, Schott ED 9009

Romanza
g-Moll / G minor

Anton Diabelli
1781 – 1858

aus / from: A. Diabelli: Melodische Übungsstücke / Melodic Exercises, op. 149, Schott ED 9009

Allegretto

Anton Diabelli

aus / from: A. Diabelli: Melodische Übungsstücke / Melodic Exercises, op. 149, Schott ED 9009

Hongroise

Anton Diabelli

aus / from: A. Diabelli: Melodische Übungsstücke / Melodic Exercises, op. 149, Schott ED 9009

Allegretto

Anton Diabelli

Allegretto

aus / from: A. Diabelli: Melodische Übungsstücke / Melodic Exercises, op. 149, Schott ED 9009

Hongroise

Anton Diabelli

aus / from: A. Diabelli: Melodische Übungsstücke / Melodic Exercises, op. 149, Schott ED 9009

Alla turca

Anton Diabelli

aus / from: A. Diabelli: Melodische Übungsstücke / Melodic Exercises, op. 149, Schott ED 9009

Alla turca

Anton Diabelli

aus / from: A. Diabelli: Melodische Übungsstücke / Melodic Exercises, op. 149, Schott ED 9009

Ländler

Franz Schubert
1797–1828
Arr.: Johannes Brahms

No. 3

No. 4

No. 5

aus / from: F. Schubert: 11 Ländler, Schott ED 2338

Ländler

Franz Schubert
1797–1828
Arr.: Johannes Brahms

Trällerliedchen
Humming Song

Robert Schumann
1810–1856
Arr.: Theodor Kirchner

Nicht schnell

aus / from: R. Schumann: Album für die Jugend / Album for the Young op. 68

Trällerliedchen
Humming Song

Robert Schumann
1810–1856
Arr.: Theodor Kirchner

aus / from: R. Schumann: Album für die Jugend / Album for the Young op. 68

Armes Waisenkind
The Poor Orphan

Robert Schumann
Arr.: Theodor Kirchner

aus / from: R. Schumann: Album für die Jugend / Album for the Young op. 68

Armes Waisenkind
The Poor Orphan

Robert Schumann
Arr.: Theodor Kirchner

Langsam

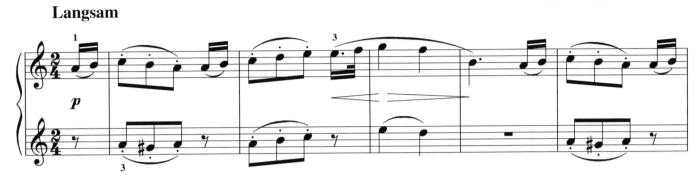

langsamer   *im Tempo*

aus / from: R. Schumann: Album für die Jugend / Album for the Young op. 68

Fröhlicher Landmann
The Happy Farmer

Robert Schumann
Arr.: Theodor Kirchner

Frisch und munter

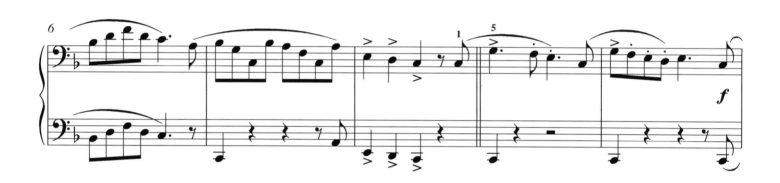

© 2014 Schott Music GmbH & Co. KG, Mainz
aus / from: R. Schumann: Album für die Jugend / Album for the Young op. 68

Fröhlicher Landmann
The Happy Farmer

Robert Schumann
Arr.: Theodor Kirchner

Frisch und munter

aus / from: R. Schumann: Album für die Jugend / Album for the Young op. 68

Tempo di Valse

Cornelius Gurlitt
1820–1901

aus / from: C. Gurlitt: Der Anfänger / The Beginner op. 211, Schott ED 9046

Tempo di Valse

Cornelius Gurlitt
1820–1901

Allegretto grazioso

aus / from: C. Gurlitt: Der Anfänger / The Beginner op. 211, Schott ED 9046

Con moto

Cornelius Gurlitt

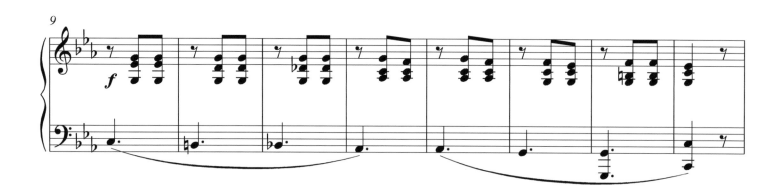

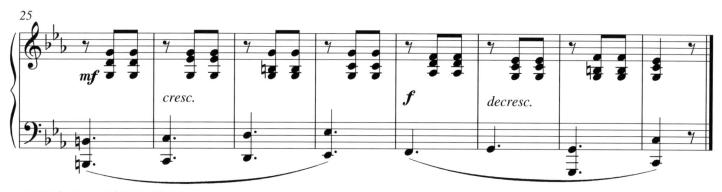

aus / from: C. Gurlitt: Der Anfänger / The Beginner op. 211, Schott ED 9046

Con moto

Cornelius Gurlitt

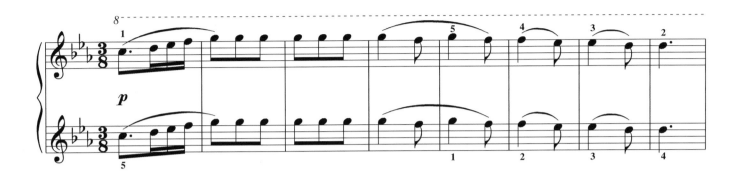

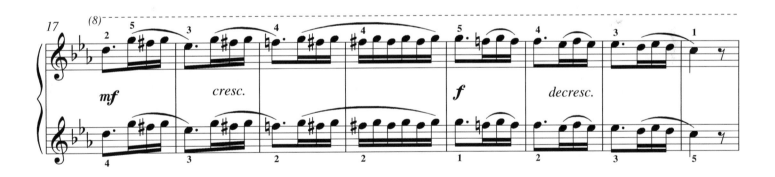

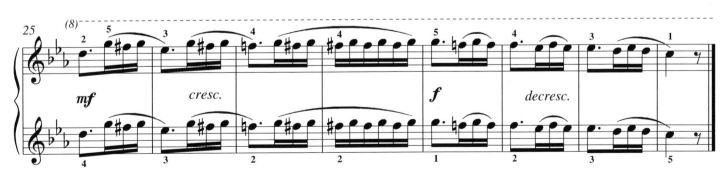

aus / from: C. Gurlitt: Der Anfänger / The Beginner op. 211, Schott ED 9046

Bauerntanz
Peasants' Dance

Cornelius Gurlitt

Allegretto scherzando

aus / from: C. Gurlitt: Der Anfänger / The Beginner op. 211, Schott ED 9046

Da Capo al Fine

Bauerntanz
Peasants' Dance

Cornelius Gurlitt

aus / from: C. Gurlitt: Der Anfänger / The Beginner op. 211, Schott ED 9046

Barcarolle

Cornelius Gurlitt

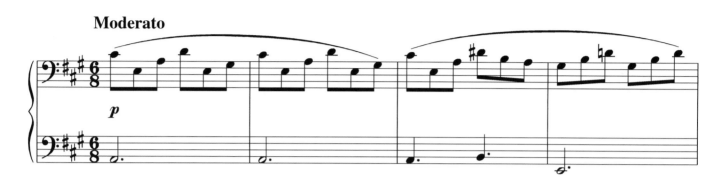

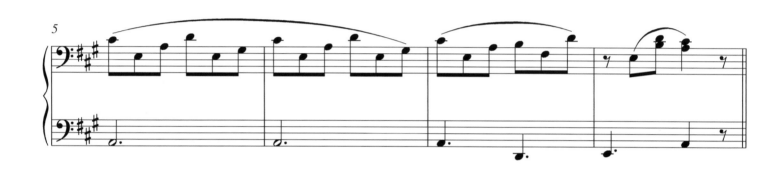

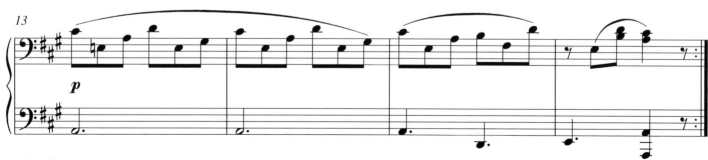

aus / from: C. Gurlitt: Der Anfänger / The Beginner op. 211, Schott ED 9046

Barcarolle

Cornelius Gurlitt

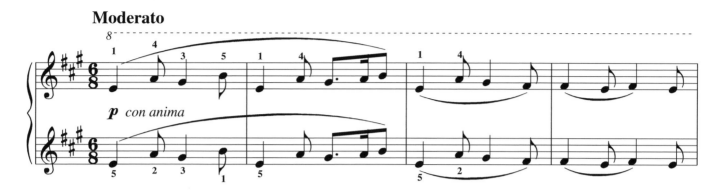

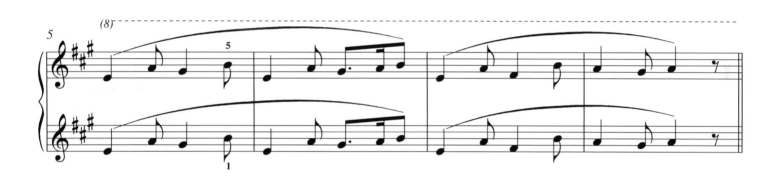

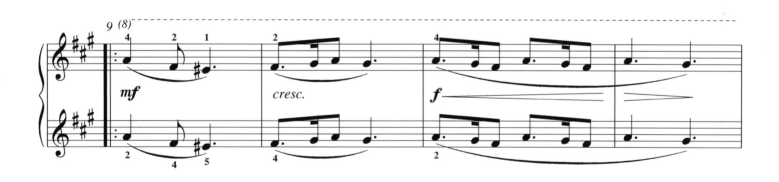

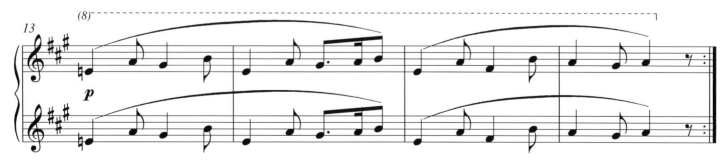

aus / from: C. Gurlitt: Der Anfänger / The Beginner op. 211, Schott ED 9046

Gavotte

Cornelius Gurlitt

© 2014 Schott Music GmbH & Co. KG, Mainz
aus / from: C. Gurlitt: Der Anfänger / The Beginner op. 211, Schott ED 9046

Da Capo al Fine,
senza replica

Gavotte

Cornelius Gurlitt

aus / from: C. Gurlitt: Der Anfänger / The Beginner op. 211, Schott ED 9046

Kuckuck

Cuckoo

Anton Arensky
1861–1906

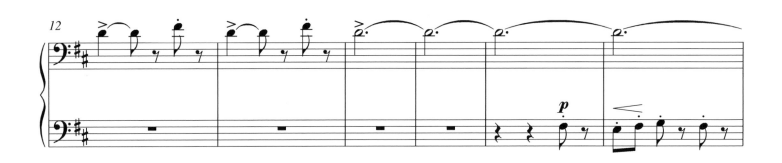

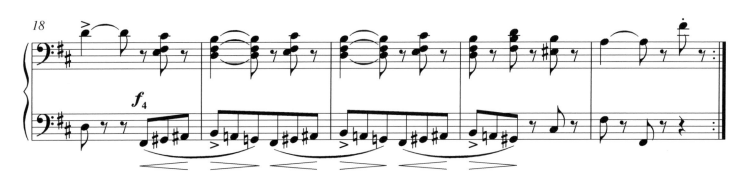

aus / from: A. Arensky: 6 Kinderstücke / 6 Children's Pieces op. 34

Kuckuck

Cuckoo

Anton Arensky
1861–1906

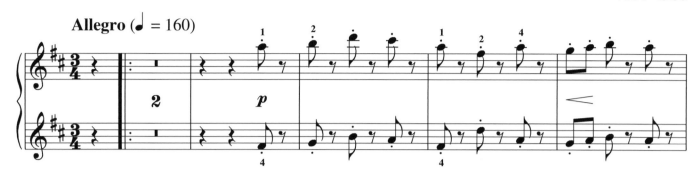

aus / from: A. Arensky: 6 Kinderstücke / 6 Children's Pieces op. 34

Im Grünen
In the Meadows

Alexander Gretchaninoff
1864–1959

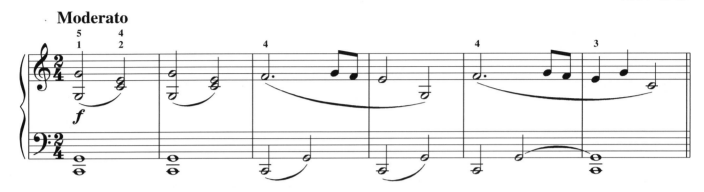

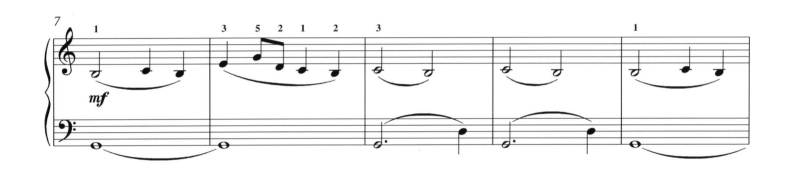

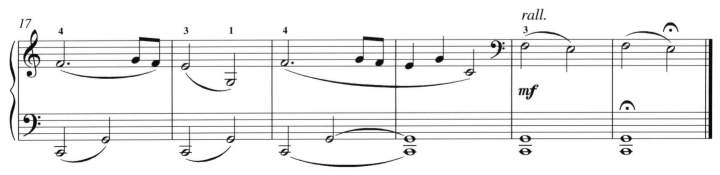

aus / from: A. Gretchaninoff: Im Grünen / In the Meadows op. 99/1, Schott ED 1125

Im Grünen
In the Meadows

Alexander Gretchaninoff
1864–1959

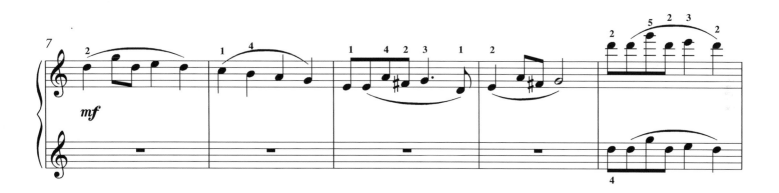

aus / from: A. Gretchaninoff: Im Grünen / In the Meadows op. 99/1, Schott ED 1125

Barkarole

Georges Frank Humbert
1892–1958

aus / from: G. F. Humbert: Zu Zweien, Schott ED 3776

Barkarole

Georges Frank Humbert
1892–1958

aus / from: G. F. Humbert: Zu Zweien, Schott ED 3776

Tango

Mátyás Seiber
1905–1960

aus / from: M. Seiber: Leichte Tänze Band 1 / Easy Dances Vol. 1, Schott ED 2529

Tango

Mátyás Seiber
1905–1960

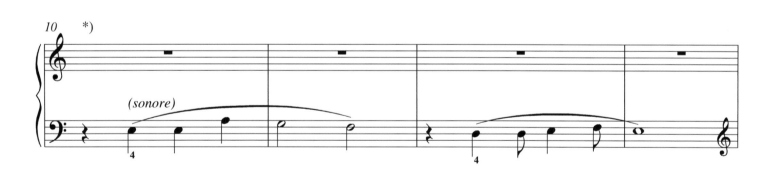

aus / from: M. Seiber: Leichte Tänze Band 1 / Easy Dances Vol. 1, Schott ED 2529

*) leichter: in der hohen Lage (wie Takt 2-5) / easier in higher position (as bar 2-5)

Blues

Mátyás Seiber

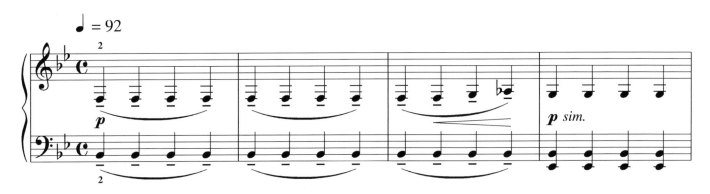

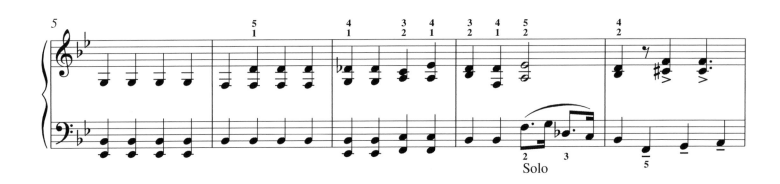

aus / from: M. Seiber: Leichte Tänze Band 1 / Easy Dances Vol. 1, Schott ED 2529

Blues

Mátyás Seiber

aus / from: M. Seiber: Leichte Tänze Band 1 / Easy Dances Vol. 1, Schott ED 2529

Come Here and Play

Eduard Pütz
1911–2000

aus / from: E. Pütz, Let's Play Together, Schott ED 8482

Come Here and Play

Eduard Pütz
1911–2000

*) Die Achtel können, wie im „Swing" üblich, triolisch gespielt werden.
   The quavers, as is usually case in „Swing", may be played as triplets.

aus / from: E. Pütz, Let's Play Together, Schott ED 8482

Little Romance

Eduard Pütz

© 2014 Schott Music GmbH & Co. KG, Mainz
aus / from: E. Pütz, Let's Play Together, Schott ED 8482

Little Romance

Eduard Pütz

aus / from: E. Pütz, Let's Play Together, Schott ED 8482

Drei Hochzeitstänze / Three Wedding Dances

1. Der Karren steht vor dem Tor
The Cart is at the Gate

György Ligeti
1923–2006

aus / from: G. Ligeti: Fünf Stücke / Five Pieces, Schott ED 7955

Drei Hochzeitstänze / Tree Wedding Dances

1. Der Karren steht vor dem Tor
The Cart is at the Gate

György Ligeti
1923–2006

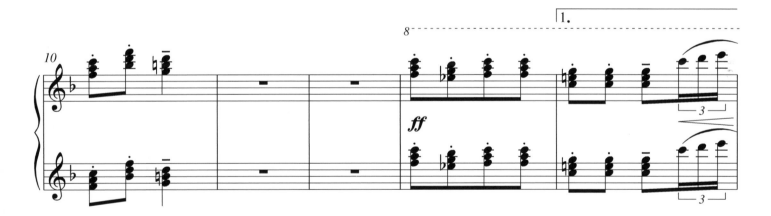

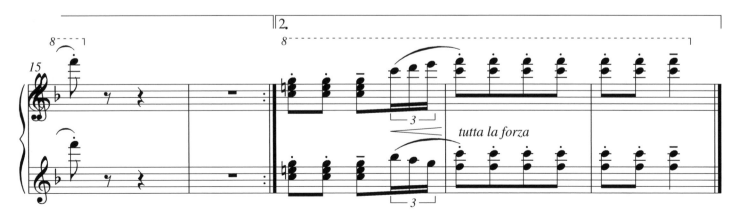

aus / from: G. Ligeti: Fünf Stücke / Five Pieces, Schott ED 7955

2. Komm schnell her und sei schön
Quickly Come Here Pretty

György Ligeti

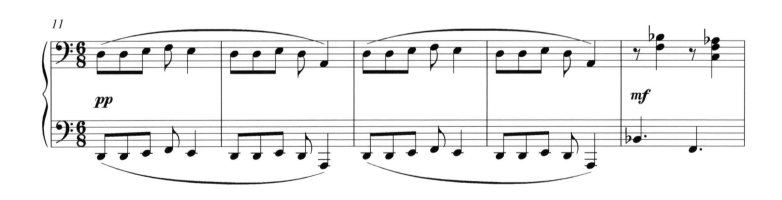

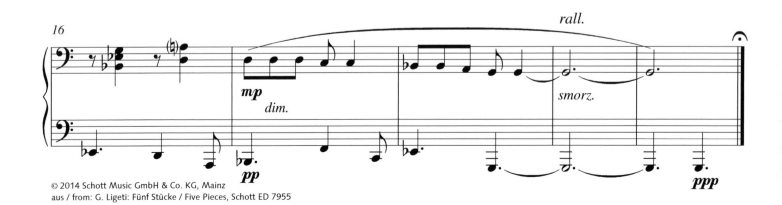

aus / from: G. Ligeti: Fünf Stücke / Five Pieces, Schott ED 7955

2. Komm schnell her und sei schön
Quickly Come Here Pretty

György Ligeti

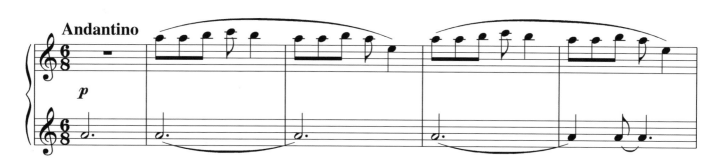

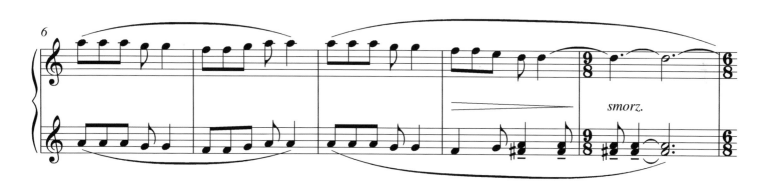

aus / from: G. Ligeti: Fünf Stücke / Five Pieces, Schott ED 7955

3. Drehtanz
Circling Dance

György Ligeti

aus / from: G. Ligeti: Fünf Stücke / Five Pieces, Schott ED 7955

3. Drehtanz
Circling Dance

György Ligeti

Jazz Waltz

John Kember
*1935

Jazz Waltz

John Kember
*1935

Unheimliche Höhlenmusik
Eerie Cave Music

Christoph Hempel
*1946

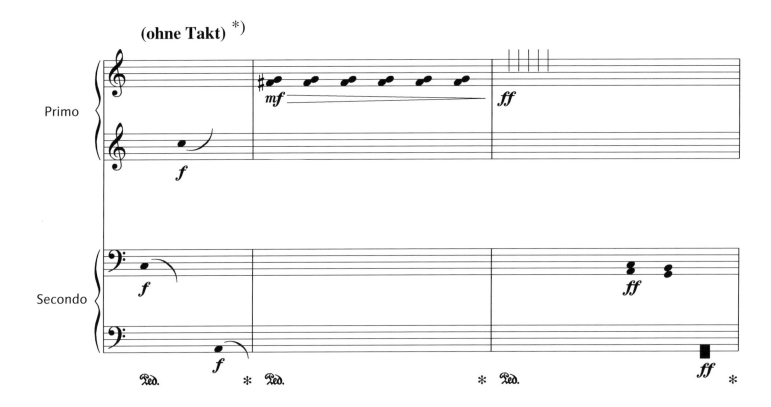

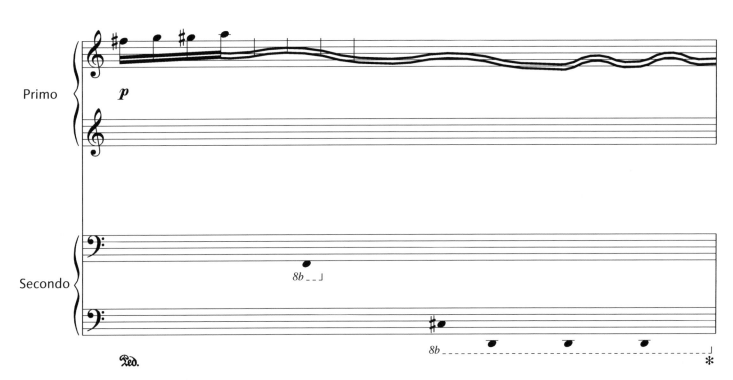

*) Die grafische Notation kann frei interpretiert werden / The graphical notation can be interpreted freely

aus / from: C. Hempel: Klavier zu zweit, Schott ED 7423

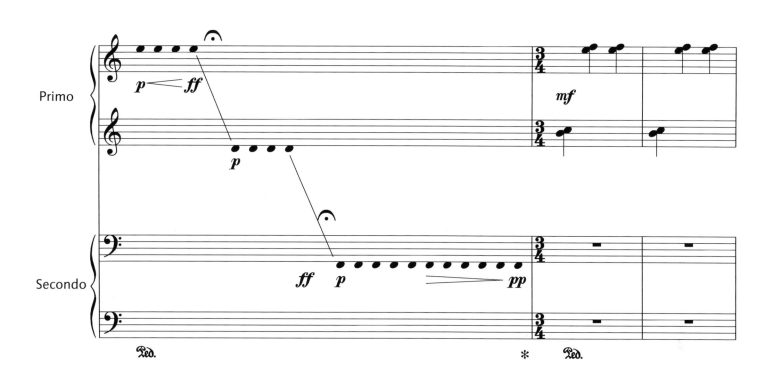

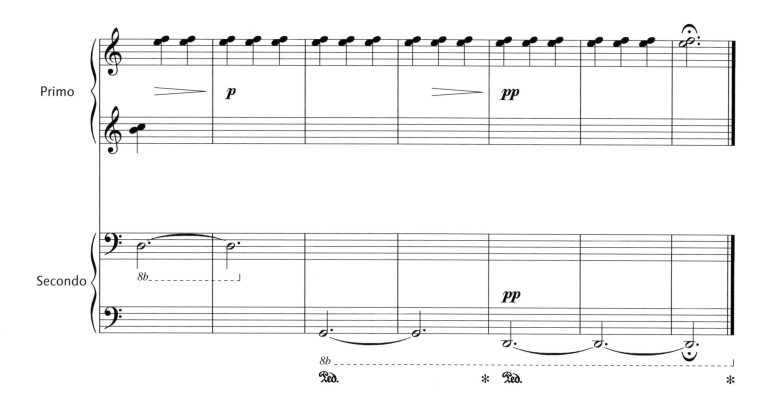

Für Marija
For Marija

Jürgen Moser
*1949

aus / from: J. Moser: Just for Fun, Schott ED 8575

Für Marija
For Marija

Jürgen Moser
*1949

Opas Ragtime
Grandpa's Ragtime

Mike Schoenmehl
*1957

aus / from: M. Schoenmehl: Jazz for Two, Schott ED 7990

Opas Ragtime

Grandpa's Ragtime

Mike Schoenmehl
*1957

aus / from: M. Schoenmehl: Jazz for Two, Schott ED 7990

Wasserringe
Ripples in the Water

Mike Schoenmehl

D.C. al ⊕ - ⊕

aus / from: M. Schoenmehl: Jazz for Two, Schott ED 7990

Wasserringe
Ripples in the Water

Mike Schoenmehl

aus / from: M. Schoenmehl: Jazz for Two, Schott ED 7990

The Publisher's Heartache

based on op. 149/19 by Anton Diabelli

Uwe Korn
*1962

aus / from: U. Korn: Let's Swing, Mr. Diabelli!, Schott ED 20718

The Publisher's Heartache

based on op. 149/19 by Anton Diabelli

Uwe Korn
*1962

aus / from: U. Korn: Let's Swing, Mr. Diabelli!, Schott ED 20718

Alla Argentina

based on op. 149/26 by Anton Diabelli

Uwe Korn

aus / from: U. Korn: Let's Swing, Mr. Diabelli!, Schott ED 20718

Alla Argentina

based on op. 149/26 by Anton Diabelli

Uwe Korn

Schott Music, Mainz 55 768

aus / from: U. Korn: Let's Swing, Mr. Diabelli!, Schott ED 20718

Fantasievolle Klaviermusik / Imaginative Piano Music

Themenhefte in der Reihe „Schott Piano Classics"
Collections on various topics in the 'Schott Piano Classics' series
Herausgegeben von / Edited by Monika Twelsiek

- Unbekanntes entdecken
- Bekanntes in neuem Licht sehen
- Spannende und vielfarbige Themenhefte
- für den anspruchsvollen Unterricht
- leicht bis mittelschwer

- discover unfamiliar pieces
- see familiar pieces in a new light
- stimulating and colourful thematic collections
- for interesting and challenging tuition
- easy to intermediate level

Impressionismus / Impressionism

27 Originalwerke rund um Debussy – zum Eintauchen in die schwerelose Welt des Impressionismus

27 original pieces, grouped around Debussy – for immersion in the weightless world of impressionism
ED 9042

Programmmusik / Programme Music

40 Originalwerke, die mit programmatischen Titeln die Fantasie anregen – „Im Wald", „Regen", „Mondschein", „Sport", „Technik" u.a.

40 original pieces with programmatic titles stimulating the imagination – 'In the Forest', 'Rain', 'Moonlight', 'Sport', 'Technology' etc.
ED 9043

Reisebilder / Travel Pictures

37 Originalwerke zum Erkunden fremder Welten, – musikalische Ansichtskarten einer Reise in die unterschiedlichsten Länder

37 original pieces exploring foreign lands – musical postcards illustrate a journey in the most various countries
ED 9044

Emotionen / Emotions

35 Originalwerke zum Lachen und Weinen – schillernde Gefühle, die durch Musik erweckt und dargestellt werden

35 original pieces to inspire laughter and tears – dazzling feelings that are described and evoked by music
ED 9045

Walzer / Waltzes

48 Originalwerke von Mozart bis Ligeti – Walzer für jeden Tag: derb und übermütig, verträumt und melancholisch, langsam und virtuos

48 original pieces ranging from Mozart to Ligeti – waltzes for every day of the week: robust and exuberant, dreamy and melancholy, slow and elaborate
ED 9047

Nacht und Träume / Night and Dreams

36 Originalwerke zum Chillen, Relaxen, Entspannen – zum Eintauchen in die „Blaue Stunde", zum Tag- und Nacht-Träumen

36 original pieces for chilling out, relaxing, unwinding – for dipping into the twilight mood of dreams and daydreams
ED 9048

Tempo! Tempo!

40 schnelle und wilde, furiose und virtuose, rasante und riskante, billante und fulminante Originalwerke von Barock bis Rock – ein Etüdenheft der besonderen Art!

40 fast and furious, rousing and masterly, dazzling and brilliant original pieces ranging from Baroque to Rock, in a highly unusual book of studies!
ED 9049

Spielsachen / Toys

44 leichte Originalwerke für Kinder und Erwachsene – von Puppen, Teddybären, Spieluhren und Computerspielen zum Spielen und Erinnern

44 easy original pieces for children and adults to play, bringing back memories of dolls, teddy bears, musical boxes and computer games
ED 9055

Wasser / Water

25 Originalwerke zum Eintauchen in Quellen, Bäche, Flüsse, Meere – Wasser hat einen Klang und einen Rhythmus, es fließt – wie die Musik

25 original pieces plunge into springs, streams, rivers and seas – water has a sound and a rhythm, it flows – like music
ED 22276

Präludien / Preludes

40 Originalwerke aus fünf Jahrhunderten von Johann Sebastian Bach bis Nikolai Kapustin – eine klingende Geschichte der Gattung "Präludium"

40 original works ranging across five Centuries, from Johann Sebastian Bach to Nikolai Kapustin – a musical history of the Prelude
ED 23405

www.schott-music.com

Piano Classic 3/2022